GROWING THINGS

by Dr. Frances R. Horwich

and Reinald Werrenrath, Jr.

Illustrations by Ruth Thompson van Tellingen

RAND McNALLY & COMPANY · Chicago

Why GROWING THINGS was written...

This is a story about a sweet potato that was placed in a bowl of water to grow. It grew and grew, and one day, when Susan and her mother measured it, they were very much surprised. The sweet-potato vine was almost as tall as Susan.

Children can learn so much about their world by observing things that grow, and planting a sweet potato is a wonderful way for them to do this. When you have finished this story, why don't you try doing what Susan did?

Miss Frances

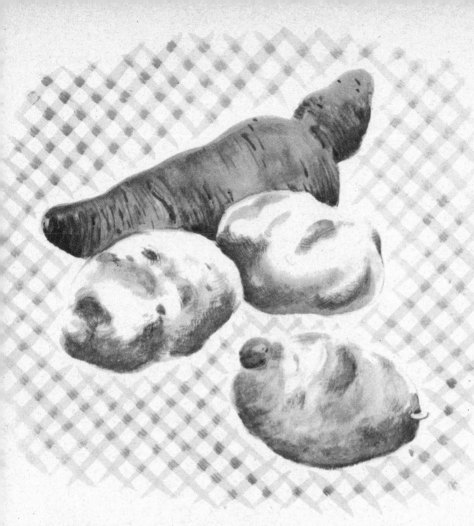

HAVE you ever seen a sweet-potato vine? That sounds funny because a potato is something that you eat for lunch or for dinner. But a sweet potato is a different kind of potato, and you can help it grow a beautiful vine.

I know a little girl named Susan who has the most beautiful sweet-potato vine I ever saw. This is how she helped it grow.

One day when Susan was shopping with her mother, they went into the market. Her mother bought a lot of groceries. Some were in cans and some were in boxes. She bought a bag of potatoes, too.

When they got home, her mother emptied the bag of potatoes onto the table. She was going to peel them for dinner.

"Well, look at this," said Mother, picking up one of the potatoes. "Here is a funny old sweet potato. How do you suppose it got mixed in with the others?"

Susan looked at the sweet potato. Yes, it looked very different from the other potatoes. It

was bumpy and it had one bump on top that
looked almost like a hat.

Her mother cut one end off the sweet potato and one end off another potato to show

Susan how different they looked inside. The
sweet potato was yellow, and the other potato
was white.

"One sweet potato is not enough for dinner,"
said Mother. "You may have this one. Why
don't you put it into a bowl of water and see
what happens to it?"

Susan put the funny old sweet potato into a bowl of water. It stood up very straight because the place where the piece had been cut off was very flat. Susan put the bowl on the window sill.

"You must water it each day," said Mother.
So each day Susan watered the sweet potato
with her watering can.

One day she noticed some thin, little, white things that looked like threads growing from it.
"Those are roots growing from the sweet potato," said her mother.

A few days later, when Susan was watering
the sweet potato, she noticed there were some
little red sprouts on the side of it. She turned it
around, and there were some little red sprouts

on the other side, too. There was even a little
red sprout growing from the bump on top
that looked like a hat.

"Yes," said her mother, "the sweet potato is

starting to grow, and you have helped it by giving it water and daylight."

Susan looked at her sweet potato each day, and each day the red sprouts seemed a little longer.

Then one day she found a green leaf growing from one of the sprouts.

"Now your sweet potato is growing a vine,"
said her mother, "and it will grow a little longer

each day." She gave Susan a ruler to measure
the vine.

Every few days Susan measured the longest

vine and made a mark on the ruler with her crayon so that she could see how much it had grown. Soon the vine was as long as the ruler.

When Susan told her mother this, her mother
gave her a yardstick to measure the vine.

Now the sweet potato had many leaves on each of its vines. It looked very pretty there on the window sill in the light. Every few days

Susan made a mark on the yardstick to show how long the vine was.

One day when she showed her mother the

yardstick, Mother held it up beside Susan, and do you know that the mark on the yardstick was almost as high as Susan's head! The vine had grown so much that it was almost as long as Susan was tall.

Mother and Susan both looked at the vine on the window sill.

"It's a beautiful vine," said Susan.

"Yes," said her mother, "and did you think that such a beautiful vine could grow from that funny old sweet potato with the bump on top?"